Stringpops 1

fun pieces for absolute beginners

VIOLIN/CELLO & PIANO

Peter Wilson
String parts edited by Madeleine Ranger

Illustrations by Penny Dann

Faber Music Limited
London

1. Open String Samba

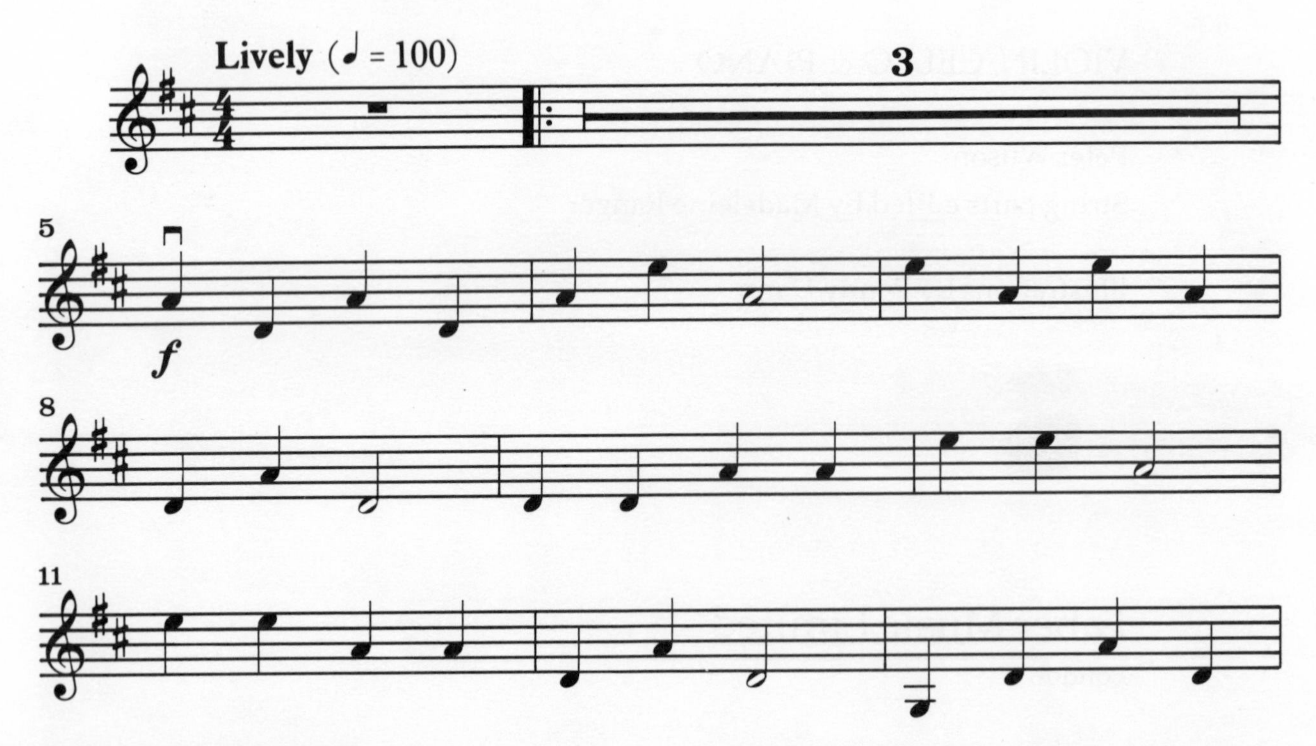

14
16
18
20
1.
2.
21

2. Calypso

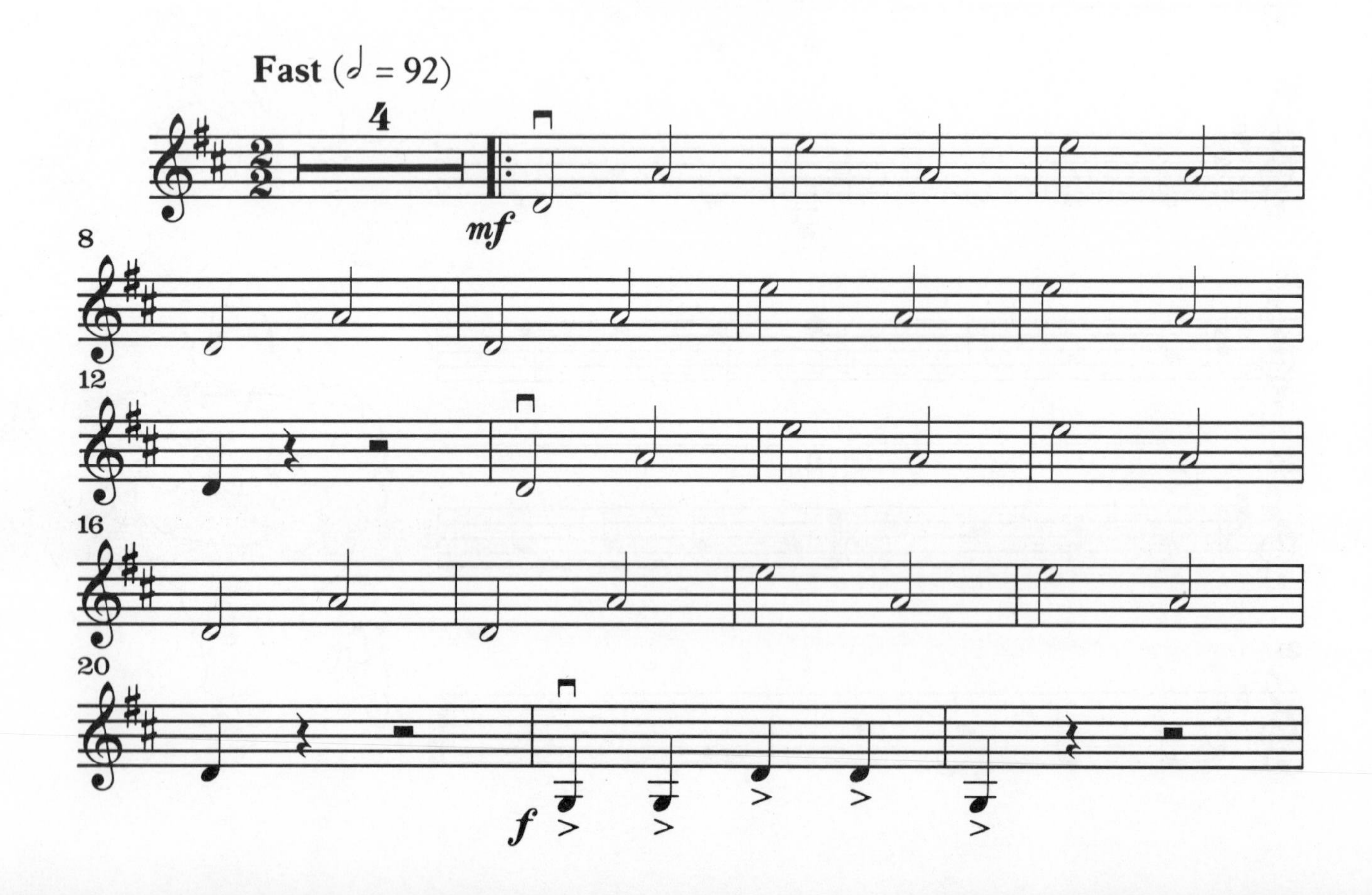

23
mf
26
29
f
32
mf
35
1.
2.

3. March of the Cadets

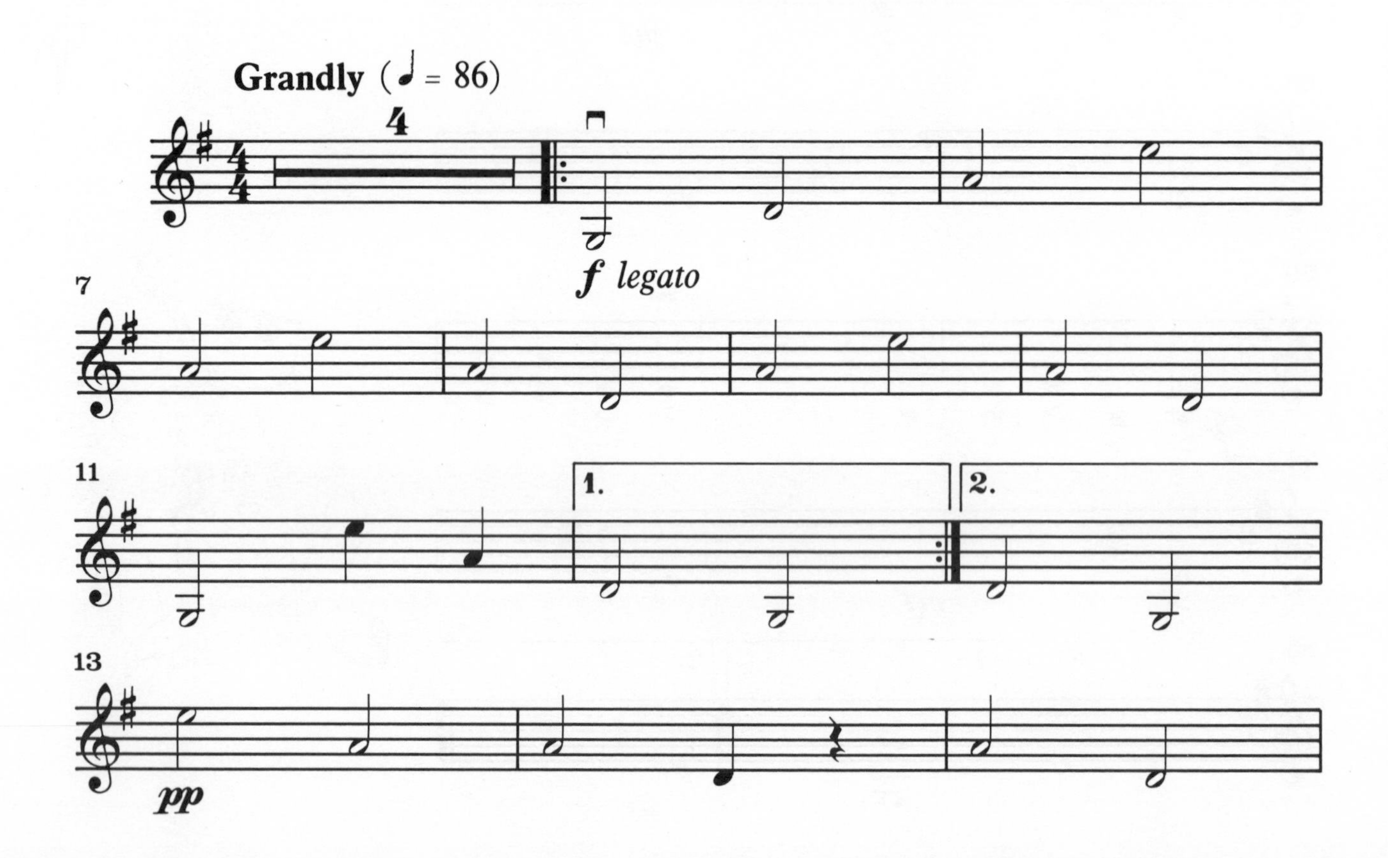

16
19
f
22
25
ff
28
rit.
tremolo

4. Bow Rock

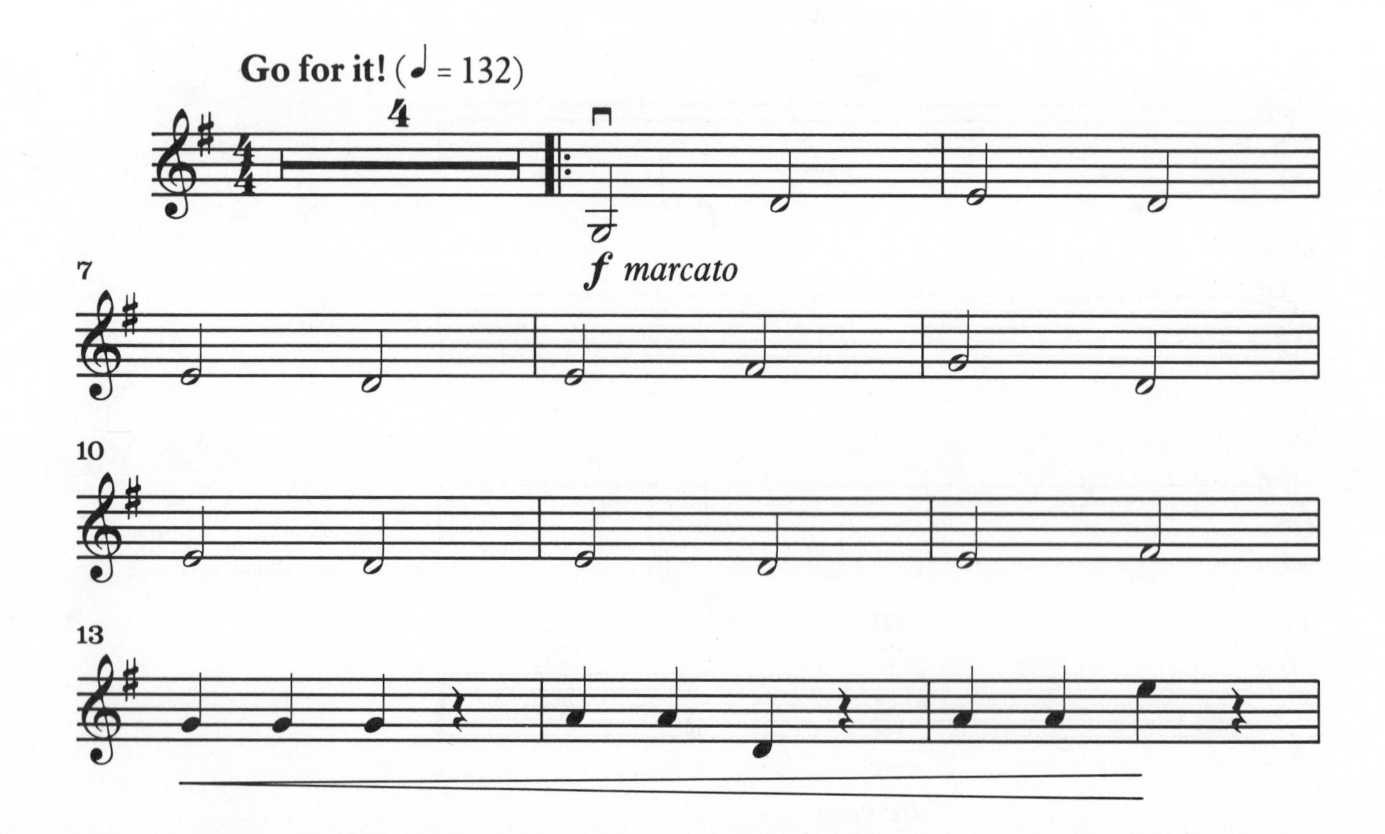

16
ff
18
20
f
22
24
2
1.
2.

5. Piccadilly Ballad

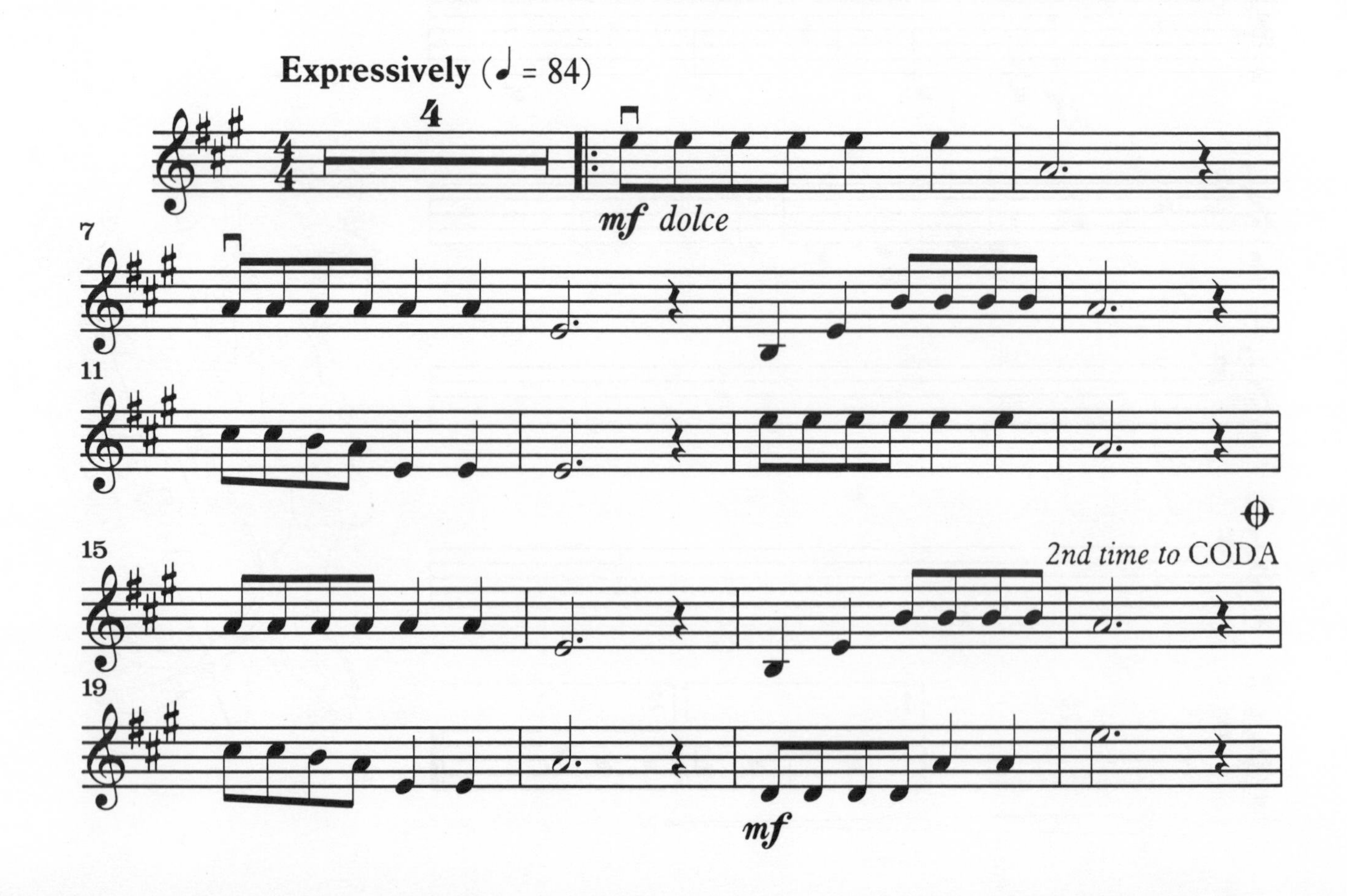

23
25
cresc.
27
f
30
CODA
33
molto rall.
p
16
LEICESTER SQUARE
PICCADILLY CIRCUS
PICCADILLY
ABC 1

6. Jazz Waltz

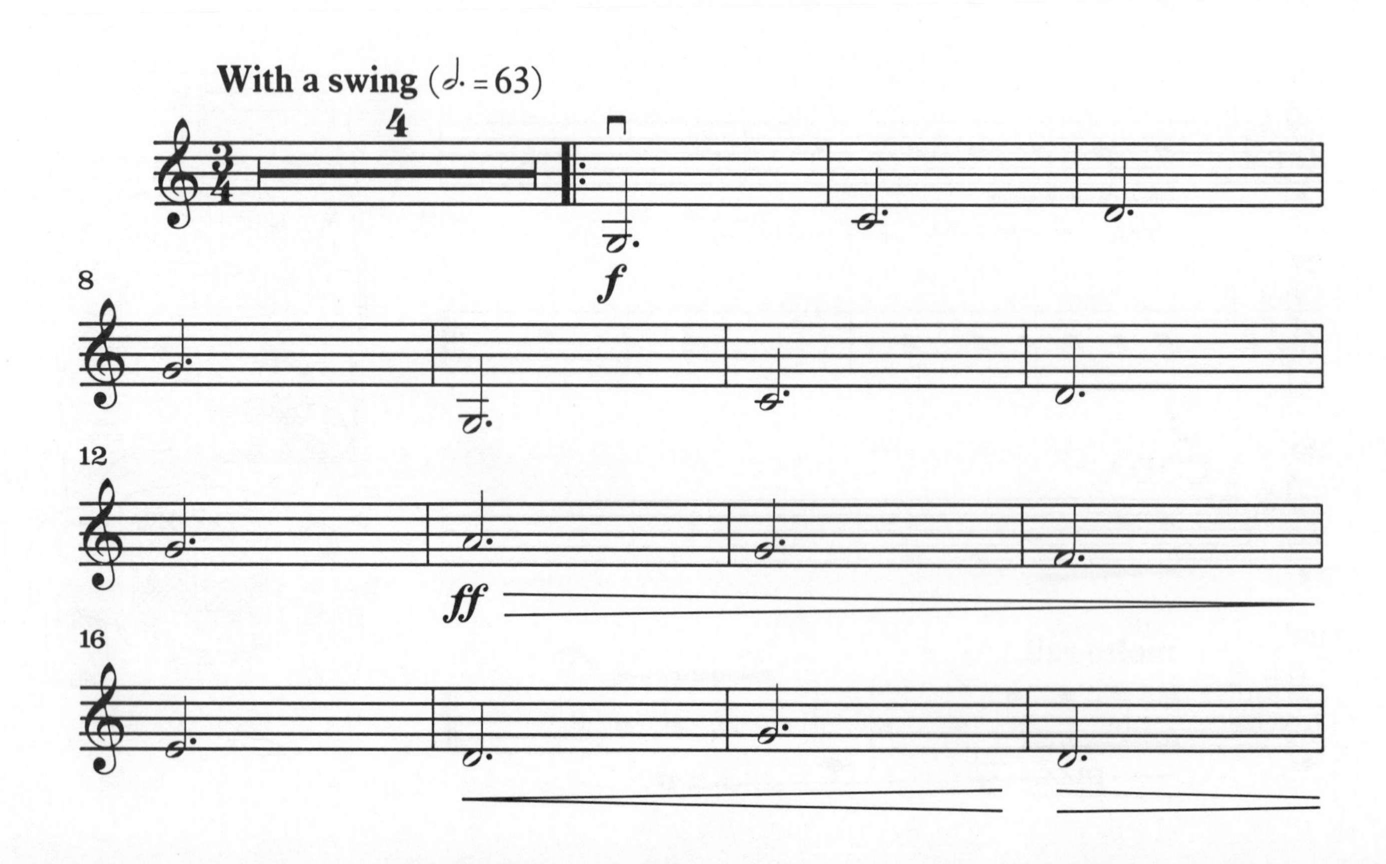

20
f
23
26
29
2
1.
2
2.
3
34
pizz.

7. Sky Diver

20
mf
23
f
26
mf
29
f
31
5